TOM & JERRY

Super Champion

Tom seems to be taking it all seriously now.

You're right. He's up at dawn every morning.

D1497015

Super Champion

You're going to have to do some serious training, Tom. I heard that your opponent is a really beefy cat.

TWO! Stagger him with my champion left hook.

AND THREE! Finish the job with a right upper-cut.

Ladies and gentleman, I give you Tom - the champion of your town!

POFF!

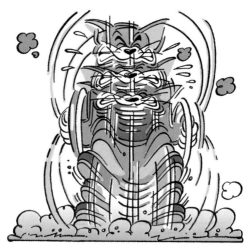

Hi Tom, how's that training going?

Just resting.

And to my right, the um... suicidal opponent, ha ha!

Ha ha, weighing in at 10 kilos, ha ha ...

Round 1

Come on, you insect, let's have it!

Stop tickling me!

You're boring me!

POFF!

Smile, Tom! You have to be confident! Show him who's king of the ring!

Round 4

You're making me dizzy, weakling!

GRRR!

Puff... Puff... I'm exhausted, puff...

THE END